A CREEK DOWN OUR STREET

Written by Cathleen Burnham
Illustrated by Simon Scales

For Ken.

© 2007. Published by Journey Stone Creations, LLC.
All rights reserved. Printed in China. Little Nuggets is an imprint of
Journey Stone Creations, LLC. First print run, 2007.

ISBN# 1-59958-058-6

Please visit our web site for other great titles.
www.jscbooks.com

When Dad turns on the hose,

a creek runs down our street.

Friends come running.

Even the neighborhood cat, Oreo, wanders over to check out all the fuss.

Sometimes we make sailboats
out of leaves and twigs,

and sail them down our creek.

We race leaves.

We race sticks.

We even race the candy wrappers we
find in our pockets.

We do not race rocks. They just sink

"I'll bet you a marble my stick wins!" I call.

"I'll bet you two pennies my stick wins!"
My sister Kathryn calls back.

Sometimes birds come to our creek.

Blue jays come and sparrows, crows and finches.

We watch them play in the water.

Do the birds ever wonder why they've never noticed a creek in this part of the world before?

Sometimes we build bridges.

We use rocks.

We use sticks.

We use mud.

Once we used my Mom's big wooden spoon.

Our bridges last for a while, but sooner or later the water always breaks through. Nothing can stop the mighty creek.

Until Dad turns off the hose!